HOW THEY WORK

NIMITZ CLASS
Supercarrier

HUGH COWIN

MALLARD
PRESS

Flight deck personnel
watch as this
Grumman F-14A
Tomcat taxies forward
prior to launch.

Contents

A departing aircrew-eye view of USS *Nimitz* with two Grumman F-14 Tomcats ready to launch from the carrier's forward catapults.

The Super Carrier and its Mission

Today's US Navy is built around two primary weapons systems – one highly visible, the other almost totally dependent upon stealth. The stealthy element of this weapons combination is the Trident missile-carrying, nuclear-powered submarine, dealt with in a companion volume of the *How They Work* series. The far more visible and almost unconcealable weapons system is the US Navy's super carrier, along with its associated vital complement of aircraft. To understand why these two so seemingly dissimilar weapons systems form the backbone of today's US Navy, it is necessary to pause here long enough to outline just where they fit into the overall scheme of things in terms of the US Navy's two major missions.

The US Navy's basic mission tasks can be summarized as providing Power Projection and Sea Control. In general, Power Projection implies offensive operations and involves dispatching an adequately equipped force to strike against an enemy at any point on the earth's surface. Sea Control missions involve securing control of an area, or even a region of water, and holding such control for as long as is required. Significantly, while the aircraft carrier can contribute to all of the missions described above, the Trident missile-lobbing submarine can only meet one very specific mission requirement – that of a major nuclear weapons strike, with all that that implies.

The Origin of the Species

Before getting involved with the details of today's veritable self-propelled floating air bases, it is, perhaps, as well to outline something of the origins and evolution of the US Navy's carrier family, of which the nuclear-powered Nimitz/CVN-68 class super carriers are simply the latest and largest examples.

While the US Navy was not to commission its first aircraft carrier, the USS *Langley* (CV-1) until March 1922 (some three and a half years after the British had commissioned HMS *Argus*), history shows that in terms of developing carrier-going aircraft and carrier tactics, the US Navy and, for that matter, the Japanese Navy, were clearly ahead of the Royal Navy by the late 1930s. The 1941–1945 Pacific War was to be totally dominated by the use of carrier-going air power – right up to, that is, August 1945, when, within the span of three days, two atomic bombs dropped by US Army Air Force B-29s devastated the Japanese cities of Hiroshima and Nagasaki, bringing World War II to a close.

An image of infamy: the fiery aftermath of Japan's surprise carrier-based air strike against the US Pacific Fleet at Pearl Harbor, 7 December 1941.

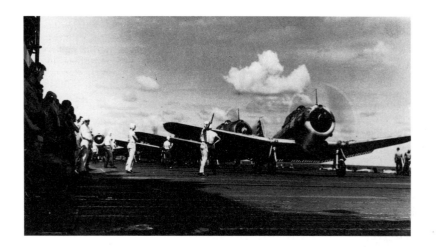

Above: Naval air power was to play a crucial part in forging the outcome of the war in the Pacific. Here, US Navy Douglas SBD Dauntlesses prepare to launch from USS *Yorktown* (CV-5) prior to her loss in the decisive Battle of Midway.

Right: For a while, US Congressional backing for the US Air Force and its giant Convair B-36D appeared to have completely dashed US Navy hopes of building its super carriers.

Certainly, the next four years were not the US Navy's best ever. Prime amongst a host of setbacks was the emergence of the US Air Force, now totally independent of its former US Army masters, which promptly set about lobbying around Washington, DC, for what it considered to be its fair share of the authorized national defence budget. To compound the Navy's problems, the proponents of land-based air power were, during this period, able to put up some pretty watertight arguments, including the results of the Bikini atoll atomic weapons tests from which the warship emerged looking very vulnerable.

By late 1948, the struggle between the US Navy and Air Force was coming to a head, crystallizing around the contest for funding of two major weapons systems. On the one hand, the Navy wanted to develop not just a large but a super-sized carrier, capable of operating large, seagoing bombers, while the US Air Force was pressing for the money to buy quantities of the B-36D – a jet engine-augmented version of this near-global range, giant bomber. This led to the formation of a US Congressional investigation, whose

findings favoured supporting the B-36. Fortune appeared to be smiling on the US Air Force, whose B-36D took to the air for the first time on 26 March 1949. Just under a month after the B-36D's first flight, on 23 April 1949, Congress cancelled all further work on the USS *United States* (CVA-58), the first of the 80,000 ton super carriers, whose keel had been laid down only five days prior to cancellation.

All the Eggs in one Basket

One of the major US Air Force arguments against support for the building of a super carrier class emphasized the size and cost of such a ship and pointed to the folly of "putting all the eggs into one basket". After all, with so many valuable assets in the shape of over 80 aircraft and several thousand men all crammed into the one expensive hull, any super carrier was bound to become a top priority target in any enemy war plan. Fortunately, from the US Navy's viewpoint, two events were to happen within a year or so of the USS *United States*'s cancellation that would

US carrier-based air power contributed substantial support for United Nations' forces fighting in Korea. Here, a Navy Douglas AD Skyraider prepares to leave USS *Midway* (CV-41).

swing the purse string-holding US Congress to reconsider their ideas.

The first of the events that were to favourably affect the US Navy's fortunes was the Soviet revelation that they, too, could produce nuclear weapons – a development that helped focus the politicians' minds on the fact that nuclear war where both sides had such weapons might well prove mutually non-productive. Even while the politicians were digesting this idea, the other significant event unfolded in the shape of the Korean War. Suddenly, both the US politicians and military found themselves facing a very real, non-

nuclear war, one in which the soldier and marine, along with offshore support from carrier-based naval aviation, began to look far more useful than Strategic Air Command's inventory of B-36s. By mid-July 1952, funding had been approved and the keel of the 76,000 ton USS *Forrestal* (CVB-59) was being laid down in the same Newport News shipyards that should have built USS *United States*.

First of the Super Carriers

Ordered in July 1951, USS *Forrestal* (originally referred to as CVB-59, but nowadays designated CV-59), took just over four years to build, the ship's commissioning ceremony taking place on 1 October 1955. Then the biggest and heaviest warship afloat, the carrier's 316.7m (1,039ft) long flight deck was designed to take the routine stresses imposed by catapult launching, along with the landing impact of such as the 31-ton A-3 Skywarrior. Incorporating the angled flight deck, steam catapult and mirror deck landing aid – all of which had been developed by the Royal Navy – the USS *Forrestal*'s propulsion was steam-powered, driving four propeller shafts rated to provide a total of 260,000shp (this power rating being increased to 280,000shp in all of the subsequent steam turbine-powered super carriers).

USS *Forrestal*, the first US Navy aircraft carrier to have been built after World War II, served as the lead ship of a 4-carrier class, the remaining vessels comprising USS *Saratoga* (CV-60), USS *Ranger* (CV-61) and USS *Independence* (CV-62) – the three being commissioned in April 1956, August 1957 and January 1959, respectively. All are still in service and likely to remain so until the late 1990s, these ships establishing the basic flight deck pattern of employing four catapults and four deck-side aircraft lifts that has carried through to the current Nimitz class – the only salient difference being that more recent carriers have employed a 3-lifts to starboard (right) and 1-lift to port (left), rather than the original 2-lifts either side – the latter layout aiding the uninterrupted continuance of sustained aircraft launching and landings. As is only natural, the designers of these ships went out of their way to minimize

A broadside view of USS *Forrestal* (CV-59) with one of her submarine-killing Lockheed S-3 Vikings about to land.

the vessels' vulnerability to below-the-waterline, as well as above-the-waterline combat damage, with no less than 1,200 sealable compartments being incorporated from the waterline down, formed from two primary bulkheads running from stem to stern, interlaced with transverse (across-ship) bulkheads spaced around every 9.8m (32ft).

The next class of super carrier, of which the USS *Kitty Hawk* (CV-63) is lead ship, employs the 8-boiler powering 4-geared steam turbine and propeller shaft propulsive configuration of the earlier Forrestal class, the salient difference with the Kitty Hawk class being the shift to a 3-lift to starboard and 1-lift to port layout. In most other respects, the two classes of carrier are almost identical, the latter class being only marginally heavier and longer than its forebears.

As initially envisaged, the class was to comprise of only two ships, with the lead being joined by USS *Constellation* (CV-64)

USS *Kitty Hawk* (CV-63) photographed during contractors' sea trials prior to being handed over to the US Navy.

Right: The third of the Kitty Hawk class, USS *America* (CV-66).

Below: Initially planned to be nuclear-powered, USS *John F. Kennedy* (CV-67) reverted to oil-burning after construction had commenced.

with, at this time, all subsequent super carriers being planned to be nuclear reactor-powered. As it transpired, the US Navy's best laid plans to switch to nuclear-driven carriers ran into more Congressional flak. The end result of this period of extended deliberation was to see a further two ships added to the class in the shape of the USS *America* (CV-66), along with the USS *John F. Kennedy* (CV-67). This last vessel incorporated sufficient design improvements over the class lead carrier as to be considered by some to warrant the status of being categorized as a separate class. The commissioning dates for the four ships were April 1961, October 1961, January 1965 and September 1968, respectively.

Improving the Breed

Such is the nature of nuclear physics that virtually from the outset it offered itself up to development along two parallel paths: in one case the splitting of a uranium atom could be made to initiate a runaway energy release of awesome destructive power while, on the other hand, the incorporation of relatively straightforward control devices pointed to the possibility of using nuclear energy as a means of propulsion.

These early efforts into the field of nuclear propulsion advanced rapidly, gaining ever increasing interest from the US Navy in the process. Shortly after the end of World War II, Hyman G. Rickover, a US Navy engineer, who was ultimately to reach the rank of Admiral, was selected to head up the Navy's nuclear propulsion programme, the first fruit of which emerged in the shape of the USS *Nautilus* (SSN-571).

Completed early in 1955 and powered by a single S2W reactor of the pressurized water type, USS *Nautilus* was soon demonstrating her ability to stay submerged virtually indefinitely, while the power of her sole reactor drove the submerged vessel at an amazing 46km/h (25 knots).

The primary advantage of nuclear propulsion for ships of any kind lies in the fact that a nuclear reactor has a period between the need to refuel that is measured in years rather than days, while simultaneously providing huge amounts of energy from a miniscule amount of fuel. Another characteristic of the reactor, to provide energy in excess to that needed to propel the vessel, brings secondary advantages in permitting this excess energy to be used to power previously undreamt about amounts of auxiliary machinery, ranging from large electric generators to equally large water desalination plants.

From the foregoing it is clear that, from a naval viewpoint, nuclear propulsion for warships offers the advantage of freeing the ships from a need to be constantly replenishing their fuel oil needs. However, because of the weight of nuclear reactor propulsion systems, it is evident that they are easier to install aboard larger vessels.

Enter the "Big E"

The first of the US Navy's nuclear-propelled surface ships to be designed was the cruiser USS *Long Beach* (CGN-9), ordered in October 1956, one year and one month ahead of the ordering of USS *Enterprise* (CVN-65) – the first of the US Navy's nuclear-propelled super carriers.

The design of the USS *Enterprise*, popularly referred to as the "Big E", is very much based on that of the Kitty Hawk class, modified to accept eight A2W pressurized water reactors (close relatives to the C1W reactors employed by USS *Long Beach*). Weighing in at 90,000 tons full displacement, the USS *Enterprise*, while heavier than a Kitty Hawk class carrier and marginally bigger, is able to achieve a top speed comparable to, if not better than, the 61km/h (33 knots) reached by

America's first nuclear-powered vessel, the submarine USS *Nautilus* (SSN-571), seen here returning from her record-setting transit beneath the Arctic Ice Cap.

Above: USS *Enterprise* (CVN-65), the first of the US Navy's super carriers to be nuclear-powered.

Right: USS *Enterprise's* original "island" super-structure with its beehive-shaped and billboard style radars; both of which have since been removed.

her conventionally-powered sister ships. In addition, thanks to the compactness and ultra fuel thriftiness of the ship's nuclear propulsion, space is freed to carry half as much aviation fuel, at 8,500 tons, as carried by a Forrestal class carrier, while the USS *Enterprise* carries a significant tonnage of fuel oil with which to replenish accompanying warships. The increased aviation fuel capacity permits *Enterprise* to mount intensive aircraft operations for up to 12 days without the need to replenish stocks.

Commissioned on 25 November 1961, USS *Enterprise* thereafter joined the Pacific Fleet and remains in service today. However, despite the fact that the US Congress had allocated funds to commence building a second nuclear-powered carrier during the previous year, the next two carriers, USS *America* and USS *John F. Kennedy*, were to be ordered as conventional steam turbine-propelled vessels. In fact, it was not until the spring of 1967, some 9½ years after the ordering of the USS *Enterprise*, that Newport News Shipbuilding of Newport News, Virginia, were to be contracted to build a second nuclear-powered carrier. Subsequently named USS *Nimitz* (CVN-68), the ship as then envisaged was to serve as the lead of a three-carrier class.

Over the years, as in the case of the earlier Kitty Hawk class, additional carriers have been added to bring the class total to eight ships which, along with the lead of class, comprise USS *Dwight D. Eisenhower* (CVN-69), USS *Carl Vinson* (CVN-70), *Theodore Roosevelt* (CVN-71), *Abraham Lincoln* (CVN-72), *George Washington* (CVN-73), along with the as yet unnamed CVN-74 and CVN-75.

This trio of nuclear-powered warships comprises USS *Nimitz* (CVN-68) escorted by USS *California* (CGN-36) and USS *South Carolina* (CGN-37).

Nimitz Class: An Outline Design Analysis

Just about every aspect of the Nimitz class super carrier is impressive. Only marginally less than a quarter of a mile long, the vast flight deck of each of these carriers has an area of around 18,000m² (4½ acres). In domestic terms, each carrier is home, for months at a time, to around 6,300 people, of whom more than 2,600, or just under 40 per cent of the total crew complement, have nothing to do with operating the vessel but are there simply to operate or support the 90 to 95-aircraft air wing embarked. The Nimitz class ships are the biggest, the heaviest and rank among the fastest of naval combat vessels extant. At a little over $3 billion each (£1.8 billion) in late 1987 values, these mammoths of the seas are also, far and above all others, the most expensive

Seen during sea trials prior to being handed over to the US Navy, this head-on view of USS *Carl Vinson* (CVN-70) emphasizes the enormous degree of flight deck overhang to both sides of the carrier's hull.

warships yet (in comparison, the cost of the Trident missile-carrying Ohio class nuclear-powered submarine is a mere $644 million or £374 million).

The Hull

The shape of the Nimitz class hull, or ship's body, has not altered much since the hull lines of the first of the super carriers, the still-born USS *United States*, was initially conceived during the mid-1940s. However, in structural terms, that is the detailed layout and materials employed, major advances are apparent, particularly in the area of tolerance to combat-inflicted damage. By way of illustration, the Nimitz class carrier is claimed to have around three times the tolerance to either above-water battle damage, or below-water blast shock than that of the late-World War II Essex class vessels.

In physical terms, the Nimitz class carrier has a hull that measures 317m (1,040ft) in length at the ship's waterline, although this extends to 332.8m (1,092ft) further up, thanks to the large forward projection of the flight deck at the ship's bow. At the waterline, the ship's maximum beam, or width, is 40.8m (134ft), but again, thanks to the major flight deck overhangs on both flanks, the carrier's overall width is nearly doubled to 76.8m (252ft). Overall height of the vessel at full load is 58.5m (192ft) from waterline to mast top, while the ship's freeboard (height from waterline to main deck) exceeds 18.3m (60ft).

Although the nuclear-powered carrier needs no fuel oil for its own primary propulsion, it still has to replenish its aviation fuel stocks from time to time. Here, USS *Nimitz* is seen taking on replacement fuel while underway.

Unlike a merchant ship, whose quoted weight usually refers to the tonnage of cargo it can carry, the weight of a warship is always related to the amount of water its hull displaces. In the case of the Nimitz class ship, the unladen displacement (that is with no non-ship related equipment, crew or provisions aboard) is quoted as being 73,850 tons. However, when leaving berth at full load, the carrier displaces 91,400 tons. As the vessel is loaded up, the draught (amount of water depth needed for the ship to float freely) increases; thus,

at full load, the Nimitz class requires a depth of 11.3m (37ft), which, once in open water, can be increased by a further 2,000 tons to give a combat displacement of 93,400 tons and a draught exceeding 11.9m (39ft).

The primary material from which both the ship's hull and flight deck is constructed is a very strong, high tensile steel, chosen to minimize the impact effect of semi-armour-piercing bombs. Below the waterline, the number of watertight compartments has been increased to more

than 2,000 compared with the 1,200 of the Forrestal class. As a considerable part of the ship's approximately 15,000 tons of aviation-related load is made up of aircraft fuel or ordnance, much attention has been paid to fighting and containing shipboard fires and explosions. The primary means of fire-fighting is built around an extensive network of foam-laying fire pumps, while the basic steel construction is in the process of being augmented with the use of Kevlar, a lightweight composite armour material, to protect vital areas within the ship. As Kevlar has only been made available relatively recently, its incorporation aboard the earlier vessels of the Nimitz class is being done as the carriers go into dock for refit, while Kevlar protection is embodied during construction on the USS *Theodore Roosevelt* onwards.

Much of the carrier's upper hull is occupied by the hangar deck, which starts some way aft of the two bow section catapults and measures 208.5m (684ft) in length, 32.9m (108ft) in width and 8.1m (26.5ft) high. Somewhat surprisingly, de-

spite all this space, the hangar deck can only accommodate less than half of the ship's full complement of aircraft, the rest being carried on the actual flight deck with wings/rotors folded to minimize space requirements.

The Flight Deck

Naval aircraft technology has come on apace over the past forty or so years and the aircraft carrier flight deck is the one

area that visibly reflects the changes in aircraft speeds, weight and other operational aspects.

The flight deck of the Nimitz class and, for that matter, all of the super carriers going back to USS *Forrestal*, employs the British-developed angled deck, whose fore-and-aft axis slews away from the carrier's longitudinal axis. In the Nimitz class of ships, the maximum centreline length of the so-called angled deck extends from the ship's stern forward to a point on the portside flank approximately

two-thirds of the way to the front of the carrier. This said, only the rearmost 122m (400ft) or so is normally used for landing. The value of the angled deck's contribution to carrier aviation safety cannot be overstated, releasing far more safe space both forward and to the sides of the angled deck area for aircraft parking, while largely eliminating the prospect of an unarrested aircraft careening on forward to impact with fully fuelled and armed machines awaiting launch. Last but not least, in the nowadays infrequent

instance of an engine power loss just after a pilot has decided to go around for another landing, the angled clearway ensures that his aircraft, at worst, topples over the side of the carrier, rather than being run into by the speeding ship itself; something, sadly, that used to happen, often with fatal results, in the days prior to the angled deck's advent.

Despite some pretty ingenious techniques applied by various designers of carrier-going aircraft, one trend – that of a growing gap between the maximum speed of the parent aircraft carrier and the minimum sustainable flying speed of its aircraft offspring – seems irreversible. The means of solving this problem by use of flight deck arrester systems has been

With a minimum flying speed of less than 80km/h (50 mph), this Boeing F4B-1 only required a short distance to become airborne because of the carrier's powerful catapults.

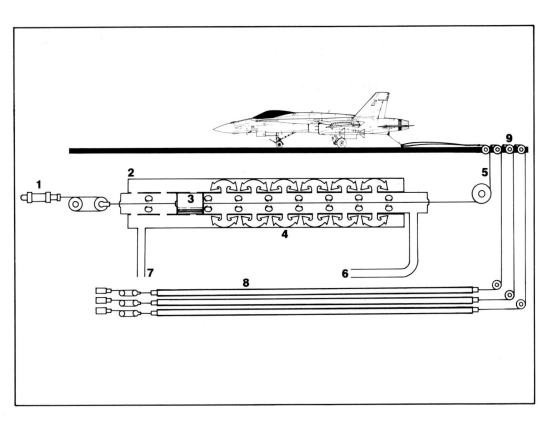

around since the mid-1920s and, in essence, has changed little other than in the necessity to cope with the increased loadings imposed by the combined growth in aircraft landing speeds and weights. The modern deck arrester system consists typically of four wires, each running across the deck at a height of approximately 46cm (1½ft) above it, the wires being spaced roughly 10.7m (35ft) apart with the rearmost wire being positioned, say, 39.6m (130ft) forward of the deck's end. Each of the above deck arrester wires connects with two below-deck hydraulic braking cylinders, one on either side of the aircraft's touchdown path. The basic action of the system is quite straight-

forward, with the aircraft's arrester hook engaging any wire which then draws a piston along the length of both braking cylinders, the fluid within which can only exhaust through holes into an outer containing tube at a progressively slower rate as the piston travels down the cylinder, so applying a progressively greater braking force. Once the aircraft is released from the wire, the two main braking pistons are drawn back down their cylinders by a hydraulically-operated cable resetting mechanism.

Having got the aircraft safely down onto the carrier's flight deck, the next problem is the somewhat daunting one of launching a machine weighing well in

This diagram of a steam catapult, although not to scale, is useful in illustrating that – like an iceberg – virtually all the bulky mechanism is hidden from sight. The Type C13 catapult employed aboard the Nimitz class carriers is powerful enough to accelerate a 40-ton aircraft to well over 240km/h (150 mph). **1** Towing strop; **2** Shuttle return grab; **3** Retardation cylinder; **4** Cylinder seal; **5** Twin cylinder tubes; **6** Piston and shuttle assembly; **7** Launch valve; **8** Exhaust valve; **9** Exhaust collector box; **10** High pressure steam supply; **11** Steam receiver; **12** Exhaust steam; **13** Hydraulic jigger and pulley sheave assembly operate return grab through cables to retrieve shuttle and pistons after launch.

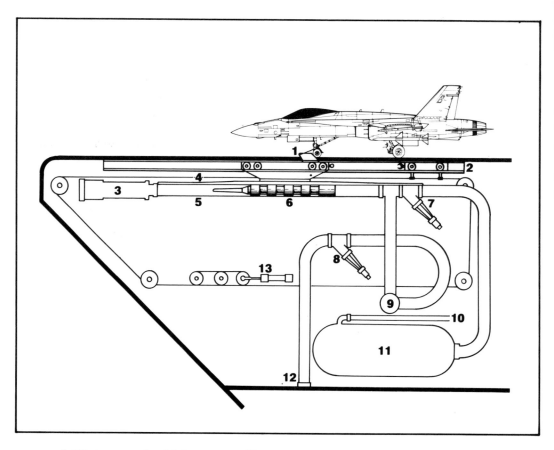

excess of 35 tons and which may well require a minimum speed of 222km/h (120 knots) simply to stay in the air – all from a platform restricted to 122m (400ft) or so in length.

The steam catapult system employed aboard the Nimitz class ships uses the 94.5m (310ft) Type C13 launcher, with the capability of accelerating a 40-ton aircraft up to a speed of around 269km/h (145 knots). Again, as in the case of the arrester system, the basic workings of the steam catapult are relatively simple to understand. In essence, high pressure steam is fed to a below-decks steam

receiver, which acts as a pressure-maintaining reservoir until such time as released by the action of the launch valve. Once released, the steam rushes into the mouth of twin cylinders with open slotted tops and whose bodies, at this point in time, are plugged by a twin piston and connecting shuttle that protrudes through a flight deck sealing strip to form the catapult attachment point for the aircraft. On reaching the rear of the pistons, the steam propels these and the attached shuttle forward with gathering speed; the two pistons' forward motion is ultimately arrested as they impinge on twinned retardation cylinders, by which time the aircraft being launched is already at flying speed and has disconnected itself from the catapult. The system is so designed that the accelerating force is applied smoothly, so as not to apply any dangerously high instantaneous loads, or "g" forces as they are called, upon either the aircraft or its crew. Each of the super carriers, including the Nimitz class, has four steam catapults, two mounted on the forward flight deck and two roughly two-thirds of the way aft on the flight deck's port flank. With all four catapults in operation, a Nimitz class carrier can launch aircraft at a rate of one every twenty seconds.

One catapult-associated development incorporated for the first time aboard the Nimitz class vessels is the Integrated Catapult Control Station, less pompously referred to by the flight deck personnel as the "bubble". Whereas earlier carriers required the catapult officer to stand out

A typical flight deck scene aboard USS *Nimitz* with a Grumman F-14A Tomcat on a forward catapult, while a second F-14A awaits its turn to launch.

A Launch Officer's eye view of a Grumman A-6E Intruder about to depart USS *Nimitz*, as seen through the "bubble's" windows.

on deck, exposed to the elements, the "bubble" provides shelter, quiet and all the displays and control required for the one launch officer and his monitor console operator to supervise and execute launches from all four catapults far more efficiently and safely than in the past.

One other flight deck system, affectionately referred to by pilots as the "meatball", is officially referred to as an Augmented Visual Carrier Aircraft Recovery System or AVCARS for short. Avcars is the latest in a series of pilot visual approach aids that started with the British-developed mirror sight landing aid. By the mid-1960s, the British had abandoned the gyro-stabilized mirror in favour of a fresnel focus lens system and it

is essentially this system that remains in service with the Nimitz class and other super carriers today.

Remembering that the pilot of a returning F/A-18 Hornet is approaching the aft area of the flight deck at a closing speed in excess of around 167km/h (90 knots), and that his aiming point is confined to the space immediately preceding or covered by the arrester wires, there is, self-evidently, little room for miscalculation. The old-fashioned flight deck landing officer with his signal bats would be worse than useless; indeed, in all probability, his lagging reaction time could readily help bring about a catastrophic undershoot.

Regardless of the effectiveness of the longer-ranged carrier homing aids that

The Fresnel Lens Visual landing aid ensures that the pilot of an approaching aircraft is provided with an easily grasped indication of his flight path. Very effective over the last half mile or so, the whole system is gyro-stabilized to eliminate the random pitch and roll motions being experienced by the carrier itself.

are available to the pilot, what he requires during the vital last 0.8km (½ mile) or less of his approach to touch down is an unambiguous means of monitoring his glide path and airspeed. What he indeed needs to do is to be able to fly down a narrow angled imaginary cone of air, whose apex, or point, rests on the flight deck immediately to the rear of the arrester wires; the closer the pilot flies his aircraft to the extended centreline of this imaginary cone, the better. In essence, AVCARS provides just such means of visually indicating where the pilot and his

aircraft is in relation to this imaginary, yet vitally important, cone of approach by employing two separate elements. One is a set of green lights, stacked above an equal number of red lights; the other indicator is a strong white light projected back from the carrier along a very finely focused beam to signify the approach cone centreline. The green and red light array is arranged either side of the fresnel focusing lens and is visible well to either side of the approach cone so as to permit early pilot visual acquisition during a curved approach to the ship. If the pilot is

USS *Nimitz* seen during her first 6th Fleet deployment, with two Grumman F-14A Tomcats on the forward catapults, along with two North American RA-5C Vigilantes readied to launch from the midship catapults.

Opposite above: A simplified representation of a typical atom, whose centre comprises electrically positive-charged protons and neutrally-charged neutrons, the whole of which is orbited by negatively-charged electrons.

Opposite bottom: A representation of the fission process and its chain reaction, where with each collision more and more free neutrons are released.

high, he sees the green light array, but if he is below the approach centreline, then the light presentation changes to red, indicating the need to apply more power in order to recapture the correct "glide slope", as it is termed. The role of the fresnel lens is to focus a strong light source back down the approach flight path as a pencil beam with little or no beam dispersion evident. Indeed, such is the effectiveness of the lens system, that pilots are made instantly aware of any wandering from centreline, thanks to the exaggerated distortion that is evident to the normally circular spot of the "meat-ball".

Propelling the Ships

Along with all the rest of the US Navy's super carriers, the Nimitz class ships' main machinery comprises of four Westinghouse or General Electric geared steam turbines, each with a rated shaft power output of 70,000shp and used to drive the ships' four propellers. In all cases, other than USS *Enterprise* and the Nimitz class, the power for the steam turbines is generated by eight, oil-fired, high pressure boilers. In the nuclear-powered ships, the steam is provided by the nuclear reactors; eight Westinghouse A2W pressurized water reactors in the case of USS *Enterprise* and two A4W pressurized water reactors in each of the Nimitz class.

Essentially, all nuclear reactors generate heat by the fission process in which uranium atoms, when split by neutron bombardment, produce more free neutrons and an amount of heat. This process of reproducing neutrons is referred to as a "chain reaction" and once set going within the reactor is termed "running critical". Unlike the case of a nuclear weapon,

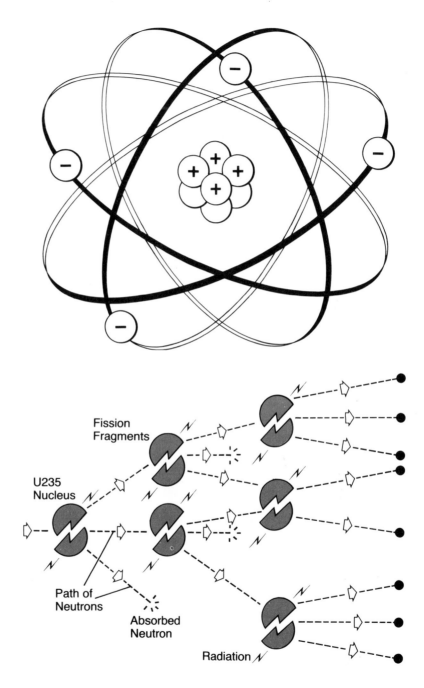

Fission Fragments

U235 Nucleus

Path of Neutrons

Absorbed Neutron

Radiation

Right: A simplified schematic of one of the Nimitz class nuclear reactors and the subsequent power train of steam turbines, gearboxes and propellors.

Below: A close-up of USS *Carl Vinson*'s "island". Note the numerous radar and radio sensors required for command and control of the battle group.

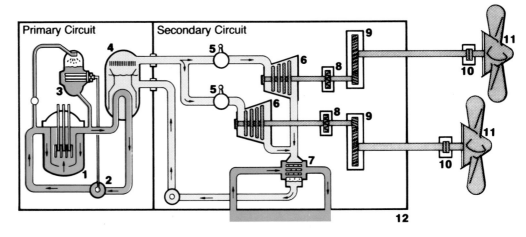

where this rapidly self-multiplying chain reaction is provided with every encouragement to run-away with itself to release a vast amount of energy virtually instantaneously, all reactors have the means of both readily preventing any run-away along with the ability to easily adjust the overall energy output to match the need.

The fundamental elements of a pressurized water reactor comprise a steel pressure vessel containing the uranium fuel core, the associated control rods and the pressurized water that acts as the primary heat transfer medium. Away from the reactor pressure vessel, other system elements comprise the pressurizer vessel itself, plus the water pumping system and the plumbing needed to carry the fluid to the steam generator vessel.

Once "running critical", reactor power control is achieved by limiting the number of free neutrons by using neutron absorbers made of cadmium or boron. In practice, immediate control is achieved by raising or lowering cadmium control rods out of or into the reactor core. The heat generated within the core is then carried

away by the circulating water to the steam generator where, through heat exchanger action, it boils water in a separate secondary circuit connected to the steam turbines. As the boiling point of water is altered both by changes in pressure and temperature and because the water within the reactor pressure vessel must never be allowed to boil and create "hot spots", pressurized water reactors have typical working temperatures of 325°C and working pressures 155 times that of normal atmospherics – hence their name.

Command and Control

Ranged to starboard and roughly two thirds aft along the ship's length is the so-called "island", housing the bridge, flying control and the means of gathering, interpreting and acting on a vast amount of navigational and tactical data, supplied not only by the ship's own comprehensive set of sensors, but also by the Naval Tactical Data System (NTDS) network that permits ready communication between US Navy units whether they be in the air, on the sea, or even under it.

As the super carrier forms the natural centre of a US Navy Battle Group and also acts as the primary filter centre for all incoming information from its far-ranging aircraft, sheer logic dictates that these vessels are equipped to serve as Tactical Flag Communications Centre for the group. Similarly, the super carriers are equipped to serve as Anti-submarine Classification and Analysis Centres for accompanying warships.

This 6th Fleet carrier battle group is centred around USS *Nimitz* and USS *Midway* (CV-41).

31

The Nimitz Class Air Wing

The US Navy's primary mission doctrine is to take and maintain command of the seas. Central to this task, in the context of today's war, is the ability to gain and hold control of the skies over and around the naval force involved. It is this tried and tested operational philosophy that places organic or carrier-borne air power as a central priority in assuring the US Navy's future survival.

Matching Machines to Missions

As major elements of the US Navy routinely have to operate far from their home bases, as exemplified by the Indian Ocean-based Seventh Fleet, air defence cover for the fleet is a must. Similarly, any fleet not equipped to provide a long range air strike capability would look to be something of a "paper tiger" and one that carried no sizeable, quick response anti-submarine air capability would be in downright danger. Add to this list the need to carry an airborne early warning and control aircraft or two, along with a handful of tankers to extend the radius of action and some electronic jammers to confound the enemy and – hey presto! – out pop the component parts that combine to form the typical US Navy air wing to be found aboard one of their super carriers.

A Closer Look at the Aircraft Embarked

As the table below shows, 28 per cent of a super carrier's total aircraft complement comprises of F-14s, a purely defensive air superiority fighter, currently being supplemented with the multi-role F/A-18, a less capable fighter, but one also able to fly tactical strike missions. As the carrier embarks the same number of F/A-18s as it does F-14s, it is clear that when operating within more densely hostile air space, over 55 per cent of its aircraft can be fully engaged in countering enemy air attacks. In contrast, the carrier's dedicated

QUANTITY	AIRCRAFT TYPE	ROLE
24	F-14 Tomcat	Interceptor and air superiority
24	F/A-18 Hornet or A-7 Corsair II	Multi-role strike fighter Light strike
10	A-6 Intruder	All-weather heavy strike
4	KA-6 Intruder	Airborne tanker
4	EA-6B Prowler	Wide-area, broad-band electronic jamming
4	E-2 Hawkeye	Airborne warning and control
10	S-3 Viking	Long range anti-submarine
6	SH-60 Seahawk or SH-3 Sea King	Anti-submarine helicopter Anti-submarine helicopter

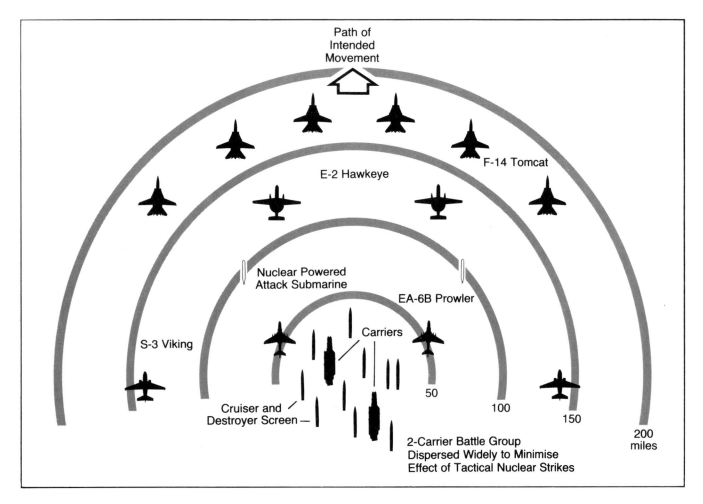

Path of
Intended
Movement

F-14 Tomcat

E-2 Hawkeye

Nuclear Powered
Attack Submarine

EA-6B Prowler

Carriers

S-3 Viking

50

Cruiser and
Destroyer Screen —

100

150

200
miles

2-Carrier Battle Group
Dispersed Widely to Minimise
Effect of Tactical Nuclear Strikes

heavier, all-weather strike capability, in the shape of its A-6s, amounts to under 12 per cent of the onboard aircraft. Further, as the submarine threat has increased, so has the carrier's need to counter this menace, with the result that nearly a fifth of its aircraft are exclusively designed to meet this sub-sea danger – and nothing else. The remaining aircraft complement, representing just under 14 per cent of the total, are equally split into KA-6D tanker

aircraft, EA-6Bs with their very powerful electronic jamming capability, the ungainly but vital E-2C airborne early warning and control aircraft used to direct friendly airborne forces.

Fighters

Currently, the US Navy and Marine Corps operate three types of carrier-going fighter types: the Grumman F-14 Tomcat

A diagram of a US Navy 2-carrier battle group and the manner in which its airborne and surface elements are deployed during transit to its allotted station. Note how the surface warships are widely dispersed to minimize the effect of a potential tactical nuclear attack.

A line-up of Vought
A-7E Corsair IIs
aboard USS *Nimitz*.
Because of flight deck
space limitations,
these aircraft will
remain with their
wings in the folded
position up until the
time they taxi to their
catapults.

(Navy-operated only), the McDonnell F/A-18 Hornet (operated by both services) and the elderly McDonnell F-4 Phantom II (now largely confined to Marine use and no longer in production).

Grumman's two-man, twin-engined, swing-wing F-14 has now been in production for over 20 years, the type first going aboard carriers during 1974. While lacking the speed and some of the agility of McDonnell's F-15 Eagle – the F-14's single-seat US Air Force contemporary – the combination of the F-14's extremely cap-

able AWG-9 radar and its 137-km (85-mile) range AIM-54 Phoenix missiles provides the Tomcat with a superior-to-F-15 "kill" capability against a hostile stand-off, cruise missile-launching bomber. Interestingly, after much deliberation during the early 1980s aimed at defining an F-14 successor, the US Navy ended up by electing to stay with the type, albeit with new more powerful General Electric F110 engines that boost the total installed thrust from 19,051kg (42,000lb) to 25,402kg (56,000lb), no doubt increasing

Grumman's swing-wing F-14A Tomcat, along with its Hughes AWG-9 multi-target handling radar and Hughes ALM-54 Phoenix missiles, form a potent combination. Each of the six AIM-54s shown being carried by this Tomcat can seek out and kill its prey out to a range of about 160km (100 miles).

This parked F-14A has its wings at maximum sweepback to save deck space. The aircraft's low-visibility paint scheme makes an interesting comparison with the earlier, more colourful naval liveries employed.

These two illustrations show characteristic in-flight and flight deck views of McDonnell's F/A-18A Hornet multi-role fighter/strike type now widely deployed with both US Navy and Marine Corps units.

the current Mach 2.35 top speed. In addition, following the re-engined interim F-14A Plus of which 33 examples have been built, all subsequent Tomcats will be F-14D models, equipped with almost totally new avionics central to which is the AN/APG-71, claimed to offer a sixfold increase in data handling capacity over the AWG-9 system currently fitted in F-14A and A Plus models.

The single-seat, twin-engined McDonnell F/A-18 Hornet, with a top speed of Mach 1.8, is significantly slower than the F-14 at altitude. However, what the F/A-18 lacks in terms of dash speed, it makes up for in agility and mission adaptability. Initially deployed aboard carriers during late 1984, the Hornet can lift up to 7,711kg (17,000lb) of war stores and has demonstrated its ability to carry a

1,814kg (4,000lb) bomb load out to 1,112km (600 nautical miles) prior to release, then return – all without the aid of externally carried extra fuel. All F/A-18s delivered after the autumn of 1989 have the ability to carry and launch the AGM-84 Harpoon anti-ship missile, a development that further enhances the machine's already impressive capabilities. In all, 1,377 F/A-18s are planned for use with units of both the US Navy and Marine Corps.

Attack Aircraft

Four types of carrier-going dedicated attack, or strike, aircraft remain in use, comprising the Douglas A-4 Skyhawk (Marines only), the Vought A-7 Corsair II (Navy only), the McDonnell AV-8B Harrier II (Marines only) and the heavyweight of the foursome, Grumman's A-6 Intruder (Navy and Marines). Of these aircraft, only the A-6 and AV-8B remain in production.

First flown as far back as April 1960, Grumman's two-man, twin-engined A-6 Intruder entered US Navy service in February 1963. Designed to meet the carrier-borne, all-weather, heavy attack (bomber) mission, the somewhat ponderous-looking A-6 has, time and time again, demonstrated its adaptability to handle the progressively more stringent role requirements that have emerged with the passing years. Similarly, this same adaptability has permitted the basic A-6 airframe to meet other special mission needs,

Opposite: Grumman's A-6E Intruder provides the backbone of the US Navy's carrier-going strike capability.

Vought's A-7E Corsair II earned the respect of its pilots from the moment the type went into combat in South-East Asia, thanks to the unprecedented accuracy of its weapons delivery capability.

Although now only operated by US Marine Corps units, the compact, agile Douglas A-4M Skyhawk is likely to remain a relatively frequent carrier visitor for some years yet.

Right: The importance of electronic warfare cannot be over-emphasized and the US Navy's Grumman EA-6B Prowler ranks among the most powerful and effective of electronics jammers extant.

as evidenced by the KA-6D aerial tanker and EA-6B Prowler electronic jammer variants. Capable of flying at up to Mach 0.85 right down to sea level, the current A-6E model can haul up to 8,165kg (18,000lb) of externally carried stores, including the BGM-109 Tomahawk and AGM-84 Harpoon cruise missiles.

Although both now out of production, the snub-nosed Vought A-7E Corsair II and the Douglas A-4M Skyhawk single-seaters are likely to be seen around carrier decks for many years yet, especially the 1,060km/h (527 knots) at sea level, 6,804kg (15,000lb) weapon-hauling A-7E which still provides the backbone of the Navy's light attack units. The Harrier II is

not likely to be a frequent carrier visitor, as its vertical/short take-off and landing (V/STOL) capability permits it to be based, primarily, on assault ships.

The Mission Support Types

Accounting for around 45 per cent of a super carrier's embarked aircraft, these machines can be grouped into two broad categories: front-line mission support or in anti-submarine/surface-ship warfare (ASSW).

Grumman supply all three front-line mission support types in the shapes of the KA-6D airborne tanker, the 4-man EA-6B Prowler and the 5-man, twin turboprop E-2C Hawkeye. Because the first two types are variants of the Navy's standard A-6 Intruder, both operational flying and onboard maintenance problems are kept to a minimum, thanks to the large commonality aspects not just in terms of componentry, but also in aircraft handling and performance. Thus, the

Aptly named Hawkeye, this twin turbo prop-engined Grumman E-2C can not only sense the approach of a threat at distances of well over 320km (200 miles) but, equally importantly, also control the air battle as it develops.

Designed specifically to combat hostile submarines, the Sikorsky SH-3 Sea King first entered US Navy service in September 1961 and will continue fulfilling this mission on into the 1990s.

EA-6B Prowler, with its up to 11,340kg (25,000lb) of high-powered electronics warfare (EW) equipment, can readily go wherever its brethren A-6s venture. A very useful accomplice to have around, the EA-6B's jammers are specifically designed to cripple an enemy's search and missile-guidance radars and interfere with their tactical communications network over a radius of many miles.

The awkward-looking Grumman E-2 Hawkeye may lack the glamour of an F-14, or the purposeful looks of an A-7, but its role, not just as the ultra-long-range eyes and ears of the battle group, but as the major contributor to the battle management effort, is crucial in today's combat scenario. Packed with both active and passive electronic sensors, the E-2

can detect and track more than 600 small surface craft, vehicular or aircraft targets out to ranges of 371km (200 nautical miles), even when operating against enemy jamming. Simultaneously, the E-2's tactical director can control up to 40 friendly aircraft involved in both interception and strike missions, guiding them, where necessary, in such a way as to avoid hostile surface-to-air missile (SAM) sites.

Lockheed's 4-man, twin turbofan-engined Lockheed S-3B Viking is the US Navy's major carrier-going ASSW asset. Able to lift a mix of up to four lightweight homing torpedoes, depth charges and other weapons, along with 60 sonobuoys out to a radius of around 1,482km (800 nautical miles), the Viking's 834km/h (450 knot) high speed cruise at 8,534m

Opposite: Capable of reaching a potential submarine threat much faster and at far greater distances than possible with a helicopter, Lockheed's S-3 Viking has recently been modernized to carry the AGM-84 Harpoon anti-ship missile in addition to its anti-submarine weaponry.

Right: Destined to replace the venerable SH-3 Sea King aboard US carriers is Sikorsky's SH-60F Seahawk, whose task will be to kill or neutralize any submarine threat that manages to penetrate the battle group's outer anti-submarine screen.

Below: Very much an unsung warrior, Grumman's C-2A Greyhound is used to shuttle urgently needed items between carrier and ashore. Equipped with a rear loading ramp, this fatter-bodied E-2 Hawkeye derivative can readily accept bulky cargo such as a complete aero-engine.

(28,000ft) reduces transit time to the threat area to about a third that of the more range-limited helicopter. Most of the original 187 S-3s built have now been modernized to S-3B standard, providing them, among other things, with the ability to carry and fire two AGM-84 Harpoon anti-ship cruise missiles.

For shorter radius anti-submarine operations, the super carriers will employ the Sikorsky SH-60F Seahawk helicopter, delivery of a planned 175 machines building up during the beginning of the 1990s. Essentially, while the SH-60F is somewhat slower at 234km/h (126 knots) than its SH-3 forebear, and with a lift capability of around 590kg (1,300lb) only carries 45kg (100lb) more in the way of weapons, its comprehensive selection of onboard sensors and data-processing capability are considered to more than compensate for the helicopter's lack of verve in speed and load-carrying terms.

One other carrier-going aircraft deserving of mention is the normally land-based Grumman C-2 Greyhound. Essentially a derivative of the E-2 Hawkeye, the machine is employed in the Carrier Onboard Delivery (COD) role to deliver vitally needed bulky items, such as complete aero-engines or major airframe assemblies such as wings. Capable of flying 2,409km (1,300 nautical miles) with a 4,536kg (10,000lb) cargo, the C-2's portly fuselage incorporates a rear loading ramp to help with the loading and unloading task. As a trooper, the machine can accommodate up to 39 fully equipped Marines, or 20 litter-carried casualties. The C-2's relatively modest top level speed of 484km/h (260 knots) would tend to associate its name more with the bus than the animal.

The Super Carriers And Their Entry Into Service

NAME	NO	COMMISSIONING DATE
USS *United States*	CV-58	*Keel laid and cancelled April 1949*
USS *Forrestal*	CV-59	October 1955
USS *Saratoga*	CV-60	April 1956
USS *Ranger*	CV-61	August 1957
USS *Independence*	CV-62	January 1959
USS *Kitty Hawk*	CV-63	April 1961
USS *Constellation*	CV-64	October 1961
USS *America*	CV-66	January 1965
USS *John F. Kennedy*	CV-67	September 1968
USS *Enterprise*	CVN-65	November 1961
USS *Nimitz*	CVN-68	May 1975
USS *Dwight D. Eisenhower*	CVN-69	October 1977
USS *Carl Vinson*	CVN-70	February 1982
USS *Theodore Roosevelt*	CVN-71	October 1986
USS *Abraham Lincoln*	CVN-72	*Late 1989 estimated*
USS *George Washington*	CVN-73	*Late 1991 estimated*
USS ⎱ *As yet unnamed* USS ⎰	CVN-74 CVN-75	*Authorized to proceed, December 1988*

Index